WS

D0513412

J623.82

ROYSTON, A.

Ships and boats.

962

Please return/renew this item by the last date shown

worcestershire
countycouncil
Cultural Services

70001710962 4

A DORLING KINDERSLEY BOOK

Editor Dawn Sirett
Managing Editor Jane Yorke
Designer Karen Fielding
Additional Design Nicki Simmonds
Senior Art Editor Mark Richards
Production Jayne Wood

Photography by Tim Ridley
Additional photography by Steve Shott (pages 10-11)
and Acorn Studios PLC, London (pages 16-17)
Illustrations by Jane Cradock-Watson and Dave Hopkins
Model makers Ted Taylor (pages 4-9, 14-15, and 18-21)
and Charles Somerville (pages 12-13)
Ocean liner model supplied by P&O Art and Memorabilia Collection
Container ship model supplied by P&O Containers Limited

Eye Openers ®

First published in Great Britain in 1992
by Dorling Kindersley Limited,
9 Henrietta Street, London WC2E 8PS

Copyright © 1992 Dorling Kindersley Limited, London

All rights reserved. No part of this publication may be reproduced,
stored in a retrieval system, or transmitted in any form or by any means,
electronic, mechanical, photocopying, recording or otherwise,
without the prior written permission of the copyright owner.

A CIP catalogue record for this book is available
from the British Library.

ISBN 0-86318-757-9

Reproduced by Colourscan, Singapore
Printed and bound in Italy by L.E.G.O., Vicenza

·EYE·OPENERS·

Ships and Boats

Written by Angela Royston

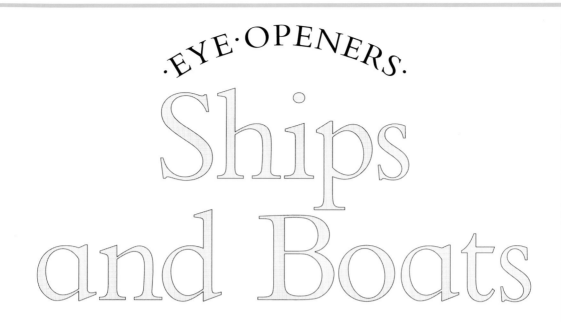

WORCESTERSHIRE COUNTY
COUNCIL

962

Morley Books   24.9.98

£4.99

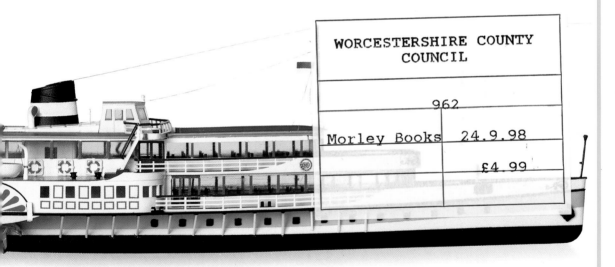

DK

DORLING KINDERSLEY
London • New York • Stuttgart

Sailing boat

This boat has huge sails.
Wind fills the sails and
drives the boat along.
The board under the back
of the boat is the rudder.
It is turned from side to
side to steer the boat.
People sail boats
like this for fun.

6

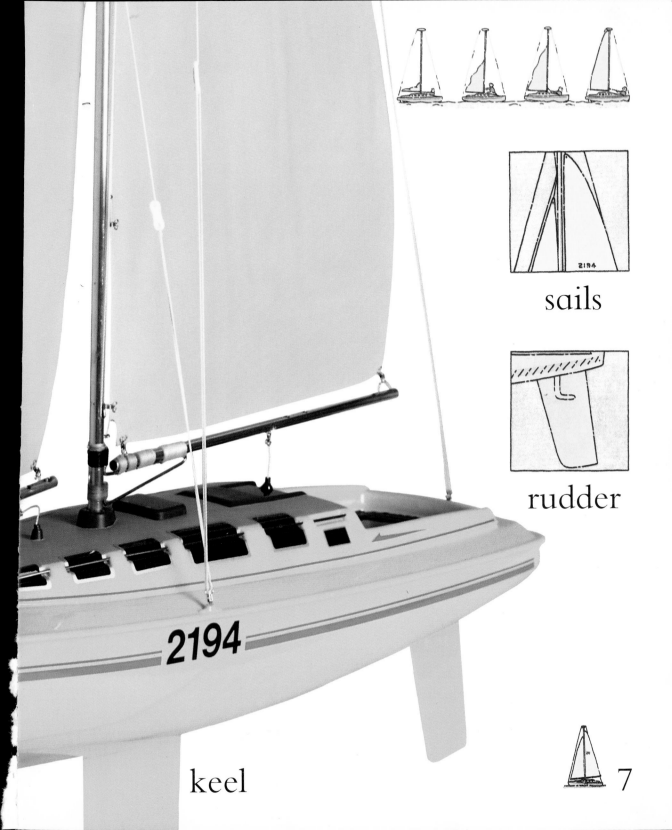

sails

rudder

2194

keel

7

Powerboat

A powerboat is built to go fast. It has a powerful engine. The engine turns the propellers in the water, which pushes the boat forward. The powerboat's narrow hull helps it to slice through the waves.

propeller

engine

steering
wheel

hull

Ocean liner

This ship is like a big hotel and has its own restaurants, shops, and swimming pools. People stay on ocean liners for a holiday called a cruise. They travel from one country to another and visit different places.

PACIFIC PRINCESS

PACIFIC PRINCESS

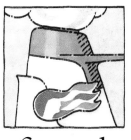
funnel

lifeboat

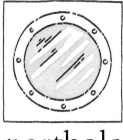
porthole

flag

Fishing boat

This boat is used for fishing. It drags a large net through the sea behind it. Shoals of fish are caught in the net. When the net is full the fishermen use a winch to pull it in. The fish are packed into boxes and taken to market to be sold.

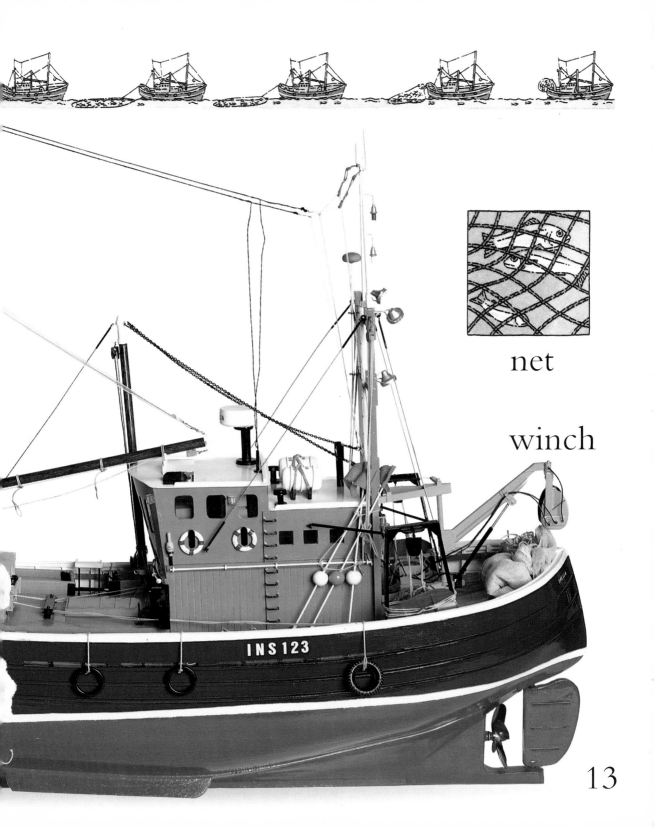

net

winch

INS 123

13

Frigate

A frigate is a warship armed with guns and missiles. Helicopters are carried on the frigate's deck. They are used to track down submarines. The crew steer the ship from a room called the bridge. They use computers to help them.

F 209

bridge

door

gun

helicopter

Container ship

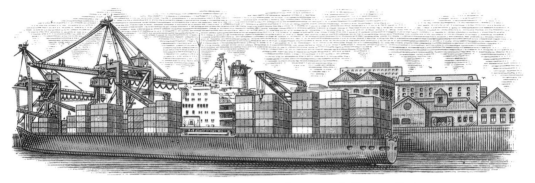

Giant container ships like this transport cargo such as food, clothes, and cars. The cargo is packed into large boxes called containers. These are easy to load and stack.

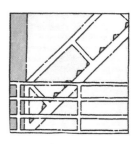

lifeboat

funnel

steps

containers

Tug boat

Tugs are small boats
with powerful engines.
They help big ships
to steer in and out
of ports. Tug boats pull
the ships along with thick,
steel ropes. Tugs also tow
ships that have broken down.

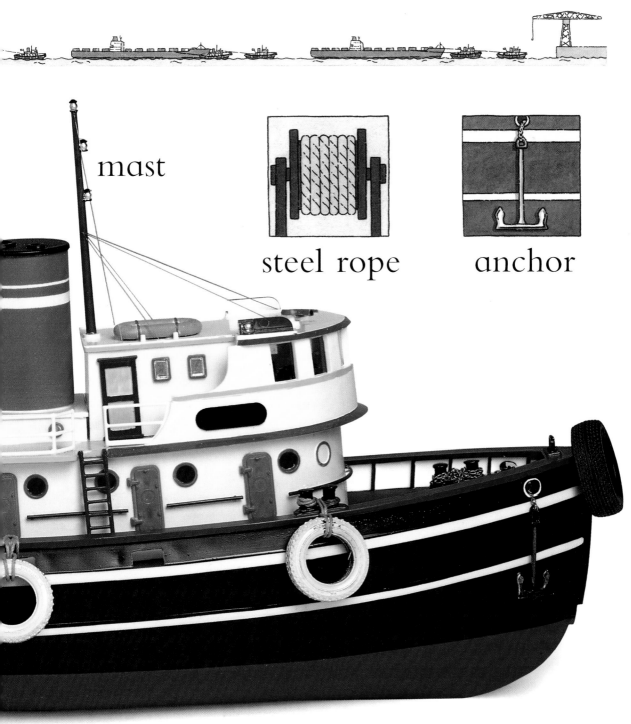

mast

steel rope

anchor

Paddle steamer

This paddle steamer was built many years ago. It took people from one town to another along the river. A steam engine turns the paddle wheels through the water and drives the boat forward. Today people take trips on paddle steamers for fun.

GOETHE

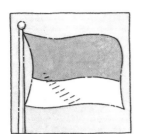

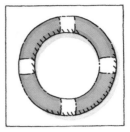

flag

paddle
wheel

life-buoy

funnel

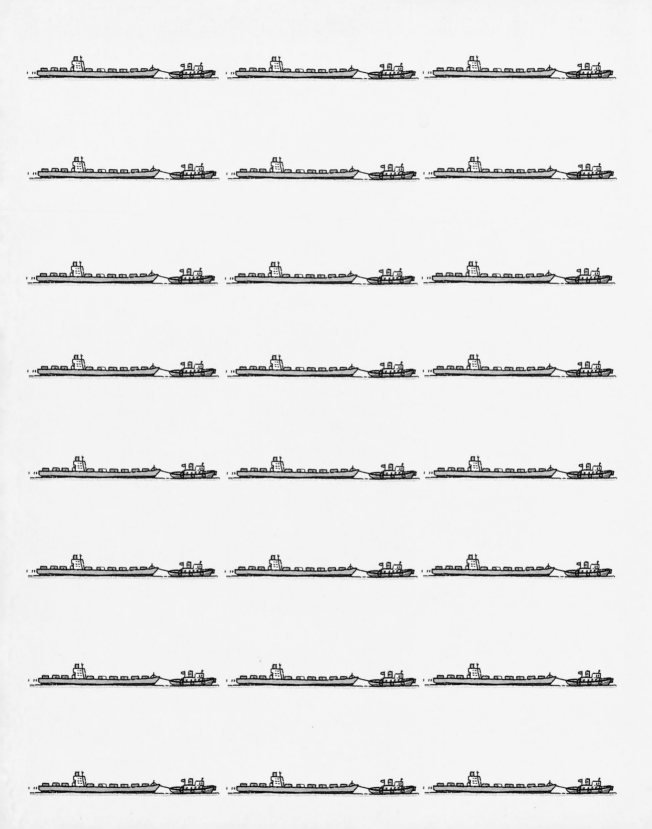